Dear

May 2020 bring you

lots of blessings &

good times.

Love,

AnnMarie x.

Gill Books

Hume Avenue

Park West

Dublin 12

www.gillbooks.ie

Gill Books is an imprint of M.H. Gill and Co.

© Abby Wynne 2019

978 0 7171 8571 9

Designed by Jane Matthews

All photos courtesy of iStock and Unsplash.

Printed by BZ Graf, Poland.

This book is typeset in Neutraface.

The paper used in this book comes from the wood pulp of managed forests.

For every tree felled, at least one tree is planted,

thereby renewing natural resources.

A CIP catalogue record for this book is available from the British Library.

5 4 3 2 1

For you, dear reader.

May this diary bring you peace and guidance
on your journey. I have filled it with healing light.
Read the words and know that you are not alone.

ABOUT THE AUTHOR

Abby Wynne is a shamanic psychotherapist, energy healer and author of many books, including *The Book of Healing Affirmations*, *Heal Your Inner Wounds*, *How to Be Well* and *Energy Healing for Everyone*. Abby helps people bring their mind, heart and soul into alignment so they can access their inner wisdom, let go of fear and become more available for life.

Abby is based in Ireland and has many online offerings including affordable monthly group and one-on-one sessions, pre-recorded healing sessions and guided meditations, all of which are available on her website.

Join Abby on Facebook at Abby's Energy Healing Page, Instagram @abbynrghealing, Twitter @abbynrghealing or sign up for weekly energy tips on her website, www.abby-wynne.com.

Abby has made special downloadable files to go with this diary to enhance your healing experience. They are free, and you can find them on her website, www.abby-wynne.com/onedayatatime.

'Here is the test to find whether your mission on
Earth is finished: If you're alive, it isn't.'

Richard Bach

Name

Address

Telephone

Emergency contact

USEFUL DATES
2020

January
Wednesday 1st .... New Year's Day

March
Tuesday 17th .... St Patrick's Day National Holiday
Friday 20th .... Spring Equinox

April
Monday 13th .... Easter National Holiday

May
Monday 4th .... May Public Holiday

June
Monday 1st .... June Public Holiday
Saturday 20th .... Summer Solstice

August
Monday 3rd .... August Public Holiday

September
Tuesday 22nd .... Autumn Equinox

October
Monday 26th .... October Public Holiday

December
Monday 21st .... Winter Solstice
Friday 25th .... Christmas Day
Saturday 26th .... St Stephen's Day
Thursday 31st .... New Year's Eve

THEMES FOR THIS YEAR

January .... Awareness and Presence
February .... Clearing and Cleansing
March .... Grounding and Healing
April .... Compassion and Self-Care
May .... Love and Happiness
June .... Awakening
July .... Expansion and Growth
August .... Balance and Stability
September .... Fun and Laughter
October .... Authenticity and Truth
November .... Trust and Faith
December .... Inspiration and Creativity

MOON PHASES CALENDAR
2020

January	2 ◑	10 ○	17 ◑	24 ●	
February	1 ◑	9 ○	15 ◐	23 ●	
March	2 ◑	9 ○	16 ◐	24 ●	
April	1 ◑	7 ○	14 ◐	22 ●	30 ◑
May	7 ○	14 ◐	22 ●	29 ◑	
June	5 ○	13 ◐	21 ●	28 ◑	
July	5 ○	12 ◐	20 ●	27 ◑	
August	3 ○	11 ◑	18 ●	25 ◐	
September	2 ○	10 ◑	17 ●	23 ◑	
October	1 ○	9 ◐	16 ●	23 ◑	31 ○
November	8 ◐	15 ●	21 ◑	30 ○	
December	7 ◑	14 ●	21 ◑	29 ○	

SPECIAL MOON EVENTS
2020

Friday 10 January	Lunar Eclipse
Friday 5 June	Lunar Eclipse
Sunday 21 June	Solar Eclipse
Saturday 4 July	Lunar Eclipse
Sunday 29 November	Lunar Eclipse
Monday 14 December	Solar Eclipse

CALENDAR
2020

JANUARY

M	T	W	T	F	S	S
		1	2	3	4	5
6	7	8	9	10	11	12
13	14	15	16	17	18	19
20	21	22	23	24	25	26
27	28	29	30	31		

FEBRUARY

M	T	W	T	F	S	S
					1	2
3	4	5	6	7	8	9
10	11	12	13	14	15	16
17	18	19	20	21	22	23
24	25	26	27	28	29	

MARCH

M	T	W	T	F	S	S
						1
2	3	4	5	6	7	8
9	10	11	12	13	14	15
16	17	18	19	20	21	22
23	24	25	26	27	28	29
30	31					

APRIL

M	T	W	T	F	S	S
		1	2	3	4	5
6	7	8	9	10	11	12
13	14	15	16	17	18	19
20	21	22	23	24	25	26
27	28	29	30			

MAY

M	T	W	T	F	S	S
				1	2	3
4	5	6	7	8	9	10
11	12	13	14	15	16	17
18	19	20	21	22	23	24
25	26	27	28	29	30	31

JUNE

M	T	W	T	F	S	S
1	2	3	4	5	6	7
8	9	10	11	12	13	14
15	16	17	18	19	20	21
22	23	24	25	26	27	28
29	30					

JULY

M	T	W	T	F	S	S
		1	2	3	4	5
6	7	8	9	10	11	12
13	14	15	16	17	18	19
20	21	22	23	24	25	26
27	28	29	30	31		

AUGUST

M	T	W	T	F	S	S
					1	2
3	4	5	6	7	8	9
10	11	12	13	14	15	16
17	18	19	20	21	22	23
24	25	26	27	28	29	30
31						

SEPTEMBER

M	T	W	T	F	S	S
	1	2	3	4	5	6
7	8	9	10	11	12	13
14	15	16	17	18	19	20
21	22	23	24	25	26	27
28	29	30				

OCTOBER

M	T	W	T	F	S	S
			1	2	3	4
5	6	7	8	9	10	11
12	13	14	15	16	17	18
19	20	21	22	23	24	25
26	27	28	29	30	31	

NOVEMBER

M	T	W	T	F	S	S
						1
2	3	4	5	6	7	8
9	10	11	12	13	14	15
16	17	18	19	20	21	22
23	24	25	26	27	28	29
30						

DECEMBER

M	T	W	T	F	S	S
	1	2	3	4	5	6
7	8	9	10	11	12	13
14	15	16	17	18	19	20
21	22	23	24	25	26	27
28	29	30	31			

HOW TO USE THIS DIARY

There are several ways to use this diary; however you choose to use it is up to you. You can enjoy the flow of the graphics, the energy of the affirmations and quotes, and use the spaces to write down your appointments and to-do lists. Or you can use the energy of each month to inspire you and the writing space for journaling your thoughts and emotions. Think of this diary as a friend who reminds you to be nicer to yourself, encouraging you to take some time out for you.

This diary is filled with healing through the monthly themes, exercises, affirmations and ways for you to go deeper. Again, it is up to you whether you spend time with this or not. Anything goes – there are no rules. I have written everything except for the 'going deeper' suggestions in the present tense to help bring you more into the present moment – this is a way to slow down, step out of time and reconnect to your heart. The more familiar you are with the words I use and the more you believe them to be true for you when you read them, the deeper the impact they will have on your healing process.

The basic premise of all my work is this: *The relationship you have with yourself is the foundation of all your relationships.* When you're kind to yourself, compassionate and at peace, you have a much more wholehearted life. Take it one day at a time – that's all any of us can do.

Blessings to you on your healing journey this year.

THEMES

The monthly themes are based on the astrology for the coming year so that this diary will be able to travel with you through the ebbs and flows of emotional energy you may experience.

To make the most out of the support that is here for you, take time at the beginning of each month to connect to the theme and do the exercises. If, during the month, you feel yourself coming out of balance, come back to the monthly invocation and reconnect. Reading the words out loud is much more powerful than reading them quietly to yourself. The affirmations are also more powerful when you feel them deeply in your body rather than just saying the words, and they can help bring you back into balance if you're feeling off-centre. You can also play the downloadable materials as often as you wish as additional support to help you feel grounded.

We are all different and we flow and change with time, so one month you may delve deep, and another you may not – that's okay. If you choose to do the work that is offered here, to do it wholeheartedly you must do it your own way. So feel into it and you will know what is right for you. As time goes on you will become more confident. A year is a long time, but it passes very quickly too.

At the end of each month you are invited to reflect on how the month's theme impacted upon you. It's a way to mark the occasion for you, and over time is a good record of how far you have come on your healing journey. Using this diary gives you an opportunity to create, to dream and grow, while tracking your progress throughout the year.

AFFIRMATIONS

Affirmations are statements of great meaning and I see them as a very powerful tool of transformation if used with strong intention behind them. If you simply say an affirmation out loud by reading it, there is no power in it because you are just reading a grouping of words. However, if you take some time to bring your presence inwards, and feel into the meaning and power behind each word in the affirmation, then the energy behind the affirmation changes, and it can change your energy too.

Being in alignment with an affirmation happens when your mind, your heart and your gut instinct all resonate with it. For example, 'I deserve to be happy' could be something your mind agrees with, but there's a hidden belief somewhere within you that doesn't agree at all. This belief can keep sabotaging you just when things seem to be going well for you in your life. Saying 'I deserve to be happy' without the depth of feeling is a lost opportunity for you to learn if you are actually in alignment with it or not. And learning that you're not in alignment is a great opportunity to heal the part of you that doesn't believe, so that you can transform it and it no longer remains an obstacle in your life.

Try this exercise – choose an affirmation out of the book right now. Open the diary at any page and see which affirmation jumps out at you. Read the words silently to yourself, then bring your awareness inwards. Now speak the affirmation out loud with emotion. Does it sound like you believe it? Say it again and notice what you're thinking. If the mind believes it you'll be fine with it, but if it doesn't, you'll hear all the reasons why it's not true for you. That's great! This is about getting to know yourself better.

Now say it again, only say it from your heart. Ask your heart whether it totally agrees with what you have just said. Listen to your emotional response – are you soft and open, or have you shut down? Say it again one more time with your awareness in your stomach and your gut. Do you feel strong, peaceful and stable, or do you feel nervous, anxious and ungrounded?

There are no right or wrong answers – what is true for you is your truth, but sometimes our truth is based on old things we learned as children that are no longer valid for us as adults. Examining what you hold as truth is part of a healing process so that you can decide if it still is a truth for you, or if it's something you would like to do some work on.

The affirmations in this diary are not daily; in fact, most of them span several days. This is to give you time to really tune into them so you can learn which ones you are not in alignment with and take the time to become so if you wish to. Try to say the affirmations each day, several times a day, with meaning, and let them grow on you.

Healing is not about forcing or pushing change but creating a space for you to grow. You're already perfect as you are, and if you don't believe that, perhaps that's an affirmation you'd like to work with too.

EXERCISES

The exercises are designed to help you relax and come more into the moment, and to help you find balance and stability. Try each one more than once. As you settle into them and get used to the feeling of being more in the moment, you will find them more effective for you. Try the free audio downloads from my website if you are having trouble settling. Let my voice create a safe space for you where you can really let go and relax. Put the audio files on your mobile device and then you can have a ten-minute mindfulness break anytime, anyplace.

GOING DEEPER

Thinking, writing and visualising are all part of healing, but so is taking action. I have given you ways to go deeper with the healing work for each month, but you don't have to do any of them. If you have a different idea that suits you better, do that instead!

WHAT TO WRITE

I totally understand that the brand new, beautifully crisp, clean pages can be off-putting when it comes to putting pen to paper. However, this is your diary, and that is what it's here for. You don't need to pressurise yourself to get it perfect, and you don't need to write for an audience either. All you need to do is write a thought or a feeling, make a list, or keep track of your emotions. Fun ideas include using different-coloured pens, doodling with colouring pencils, or even writing how you feel in poetry. So smudge away, cross stuff out and mess up that pretty page, but get the words out there. Once you get started, the writing will flow.

It might help if you take a minute or two to slow down and bring your awareness inwards before you start writing anything. Perhaps take some time to breathe and disconnect from whatever is pulling you out of the present moment. Use the space to write down what is distracting you, so you can tell your mind, 'Look, I know, and I've written it down! So you can stop reminding me!' You could ask yourself 'What do I need to know today?' and then listen to your inner wisdom and write that down as if you're taking dictation from a wise friend who is speaking to you. You could also write down what went well for you that day and what didn't, so you can remember what you would prefer to do the next time.

You could also rewrite the affirmation for the day or write a new one where one isn't present. Use the diary to write about what you need to do to look after you, or simply write in your appointments and your plans.

If you want to go deeper, you can use the following prompts and see where they lead you: Today I feel … Today I know … Today I believe … Today I am … Today I want … Today I wish …

You've got a whole year ahead of you, and lots of ideas and opportunities. Try them all, or only a few. Above all, please be patient with yourself. It's all here for you, so take your time and use this diary as you wish, in a way that feels right for you.

SETTING YOUR INTENTION

Setting an intention for the year is a very powerful thing to do. Some people like to choose a single word for the year as a general theme, such as empowerment, joy, connection or growth. I like to make it a little more specific by writing down a statement or a paragraph that I can come back to time and time again. The beauty of setting an intention is that it can change and grow as you change and grow. The power behind it comes with your awareness of it.

Here's an example of an intention for the year that you can use, but it is better if you write one yourself.

This year I will learn how to ground and anchor myself so I can feel safe and relax at a deeper level. I want to let go of layers of emotional pain so I can feel light and free. With patience and self-compassion, I will allow myself to feel what I am feeling, and I will learn how to accept myself completely as I am. I want to show up for myself, take better care of myself and never reject or hurt myself again. When I have love in my heart, I send out love to the world.

My intention for my healing journey for 2020:

AWARENESS AND PRESENCE

To seek vibrancy, to look for the yes, to discover the wonder, you need to be present in the moment so you can experience it.

'And above all, watch with glittering eyes the whole world around you because the greatest secrets are always hidden in the most unlikely places. Those who don't believe in magic will never find it.'

Roald Dahl

JANUARY

This year I set my intention to bring more of my presence into my life. I will start by observing myself without judgement or expectation, so I can become more aware of what I am doing when I run on autopilot. I will allow myself to feel difficult emotions and breathe them out of my body, instead of running away from them. I know I enjoy life more when I am present to it, yet I acknowledge my tendency to drift out of the moment. There are more things distracting me than I realise. When I'm distracted, I don't make healthy choices and I miss opportunities for joy. This month I allow myself to notice what draws me away from myself, so I can gently pull myself back in again by focusing on my breath. I feel connected to Earth and I know I am safe. I am excited for what this year is going to bring. I want to improve the quality of my life so I can really experience all of it. I know that being more present in my body and in the moment is the first step.

EXERCISE

I catch myself outside of myself, so I slow down and listen to my breathing. I hear my heart beat and notice where my breath is coming from. With every breath I bring my awareness deeper into my body. I feel my feet on the ground and, taking a breath each time, I bring the focus of my awareness deeply into each part of my body. With each long, slow breath, I allow myself to come more into my body and more into the present moment.

GOING DEEPER

When you're in the moment, allow yourself to feel what you're feeling. Know you can gently breathe out any difficult emotions while feeling the support of your feet on the ground, and that you can stop whenever you want to. Breathe in peace and soften; breathe out any emotional pain you're carrying into the ground. Just do five breaths, then let it go. Come back and do this exercise as often as you want.

WEDNESDAY 1

I am not my emotions, I am experiencing my emotions

THURSDAY 2

FRIDAY 3

It is safe to be here, it is safe to relax

SATURDAY 4

SUNDAY 5

I allow myself to observe myself without judgement

MONDAY 6

I feel the ground beneath me and breathe out any difficult emotions

TUESDAY 7

I accept myself just as I am in this moment

WEDNESDAY 8

I slow down and become more aware of what I am choosing

THURSDAY 9

I can let go of how I think things are and see them as they really are

FRIDAY 10

I pull my awareness out of distractions and back into my body

SATURDAY 11

I am grateful for my body and I am learning how to give it what it needs

SUNDAY 12

MONDAY 13

I am not afraid to experience all of my emotions

TUESDAY 14

There is great beauty in small things

WEDNESDAY 15

There is great beauty in small things

THURSDAY 16

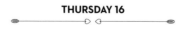

I have no need to cause myself emotional pain

FRIDAY 17

My body is flowing and changing all the time

SATURDAY 18

SUNDAY 19

I forgive myself for making mistakes

MONDAY 20

When I am at peace with myself, I am at peace with the world

TUESDAY 21

When I bring myself into the present moment, I can sense the magic in the world

WEDNESDAY 22

What I want and what I need are not always the same thing

THURSDAY 23

FRIDAY 24

I am patient and tolerant with myself

SATURDAY 25

I am not my thoughts, I am experiencing my thoughts

SUNDAY 26

I do not need to save the world, I can only save myself

MONDAY 27

When I make space for myself, I have more space for other people

TUESDAY 28

There is plenty of time for me to learn what I have to learn

WEDNESDAY 29

I breathe, slow down, and connect to a source of peace

THURSDAY 30

I take the pressure off myself to get everything done today

FRIDAY 31

I make all of my choices from a place of love

Today I make all of my choices from a place of love

NOTES ON AWARENESS AND PRESENCE

January

WAS THIS MONTH'S EXERCISE OF USE TO YOU? HOW OFTEN DID YOU COME BACK TO IT?
WOULD YOU KEEP DOING IT IN THE DAYS TO COME? WHY?

LIST FIVE RESOURCES, INCLUDING FRIENDS, THAT YOU HAVE TO SUPPORT YOU
IF YOU'RE HAVING AN EMOTIONAL DAY.

WHAT WAS THE MOST HELPFUL AND USEFUL THING YOU LEARNED THIS MONTH?

CLEARING AND CLEANSING

We create new pieces of ourselves to please others. We hide away pieces because we feel we don't fit in. Healing is the process where we reclaim all the parts of ourselves that we hid and let all that is not truly a part of us fall away.

'Sometimes letting things go is an act of far greater power than defending or hanging on.'

Eckhart Tolle

FEBRUARY

I'm ready to more fully support myself on my healing journey. I dedicate this month to creating stable ground so I feel balanced. Then I can really let go of the things, patterns and behaviours that I no longer need. I give myself permission to discover the parts of me that got left behind when life got too serious or dangerous. All the parts of me need attention, so I open a healing space in my heart and offer myself compassion. I realise for my life to be different something has to change. I'm ready to take advantage of the energies the Universe brings to accelerate my growth, and step into my full potential. I'm not afraid to grow, to feel, to let go, or to heal. This is my beautiful and only life as me, and I choose to stop surviving and start living.

EXERCISE

I imagine myself in a hot-air balloon weighed down by all the emotional pain I have carried during my life. Each weight appears as a sandbag – some are big, some are small. As I relax, I notice some of these bags contain stones, shards of glass, pieces of metal. I focus on one bag and ask it if it's ready to leave. If I feel no, I ask it what it wants to tell me, and I listen. I ask again. When it says yes, I say thank you and it dissolves away. My hot-air balloon gently rises. I come into balance with the new height and choose another bag. When I am ready, I bring my awareness back into my body, and back into the room where I am.

GOING DEEPER

This month is a great opportunity to throw out sentimental items that create feelings of heaviness in you, so you can feel lighter and free. If you don't love them, don't keep them. Give them to charity or put them in a box and store them somewhere safe if you're not ready to throw them away. Having these objects outside of your day-to-day frame of vision can really clear a space for healing.

SATURDAY 1

The ground is beneath me, the sky is above me. I am held

SUNDAY 2

MONDAY 3

I separate myself from my ideas of who I think I am and allow myself to learn who I really am

TUESDAY 4

I connect to my happy inner child and remember how magical life used to be

WEDNESDAY 5

I give myself permission to feel good

THURSDAY 6

Obligation and guilt no longer have power over me

FRIDAY 7

I allow myself to express myself out loud

SATURDAY 8

Not everyone will like me and that's okay with me

SUNDAY 9

MONDAY 10

I give myself permission to be myself completely

TUESDAY 11

I can feel a yes deep inside my body when I say yes out loud

WEDNESDAY 12

I listen to my body and my intuition and I am starting to trust it more

THURSDAY 13

I can always make time in my day for peace

FRIDAY 14

I enjoy spending time with my friends, and I enjoy spending time on my own

SATURDAY 15

I let go of my worries and bring myself into the present moment

SUNDAY 16

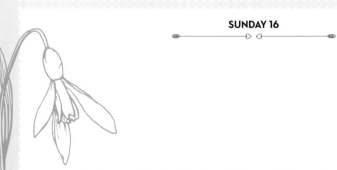

I allow myself to feel what I am feeling and then to let it move through me

MONDAY 17

TUESDAY 18

I unhook my energy from anything outside of me and bring it back to me

WEDNESDAY 19

I am patient and kind with myself

THURSDAY 20

I make the time to bring myself back to my centre

FRIDAY 21

I am compassionate and kind with myself

SATURDAY 22

I allow love to flow through me and out from me

SUNDAY 23

I am learning the difference between what I need and what I want

MONDAY 24

I step away from drama and choose peace instead

TUESDAY 25

I am the centre of my Universe

WEDNESDAY 26

I have good, strong, energetic boundaries

THURSDAY 27

I bring myself back to my centre and connect my feet to the ground

FRIDAY 28

I breathe out stress and breathe in peace

SATURDAY 29

NOTES ON CLEARING AND CLEANSING

February

MAKE A LIST OF ALL THE ROLES YOU PLAY IN YOUR LIFE – FAMILY, WORK, HOBBIES, ETC.
DO YOU BEHAVE DIFFERENTLY WHEN YOU'RE PLAYING EACH OF THESE ROLES?
DO ANY OF THESE ROLES CAUSE YOU ANXIETY? IF SO, WHY?

WHAT IS THE SAME ABOUT YOU NO MATTER WHAT ROLE YOU ARE PLAYING?

GROUNDING AND HEALING

When we feel held by Mother Earth we can relax and unfold and discover the beauty of what it is that we are truly made of.

'We are not separate from this Earth; we are a part of it, whether we fully feel it in our bodies yet or not.'

Sharon Blackie

MARCH

When I think about grounding, I visualise large rocks, tree roots, deep luscious Earth. Darkness and nurturing, the feeling of being held. This month I will allow Mother Earth to hold me as I unfold and allow myself to heal. I know that healing means letting go of all that is not me, and that can hurt. I need to deliberately make space for me to be myself, so I can accept all the parts of me. Already this year I have started this process and I am beginning to see myself as I really am. When I feel held, I can go deeper and release more of the things that are not me. When I discover what they are, I am grateful to them for the lessons they have brought me. As I experience the relief of letting go, I connect to the lightness and potential of what is to come.

EXERCISE

I slow down and bring my awareness into my body. In my mind's eye I see myself in nature, somewhere I feel safe. Each time it's different – a beautiful garden, a beach, a mountain top, a river. I imagine that I am there right now: I sit on the ground with my back to a tree or a rock and feel held. I can feel the ground beneath me, and tension leaves my body. I soften my shoulders, relax my chest and stomach, and know that I am doing the best that I can. When I am soft and more peaceful, I feel my energy drawing itself down into the Earth, like roots, so that I am grounded and held.

GOING DEEPER

Do the exercise outside. When you feel grounded, imagine yourself expanding your energy outwards and upwards, reaching up like the branches of a tree to the sky. Free yourself and allow yourself to be the bright shining light that you are. Connect to a source of Universal love and breathe it down through your head, into your body. Ground yourself deeper into the Earth. With every breath you are healing, with every breath you relax even more.

SUNDAY 1

I feel safe to be here

MONDAY 2

I slow down and breathe and connect to Mother Earth

TUESDAY 3

WEDNESDAY 4

I allow myself to look after myself

THURSDAY 5

I anchor myself to the ground and let go of my troubles

FRIDAY 6

SATURDAY 7

I give myself the space to rest when needed

SUNDAY 8

If it is important and for me, it will not pass me by

MONDAY 9

TUESDAY 10

I am learning to love all of the parts of myself

WEDNESDAY 11

I no longer need to pretend to be something that I am not

THURSDAY 12

When I make space for compassion, I make space for healing

FRIDAY 13

SATURDAY 14

I breathe in peace and breathe out all that is not peace

SUNDAY 15

Everyone is doing the best they can with what they know at this time, including me

MONDAY 16

I am ready to experience the joy, beauty and love that is here for me

TUESDAY 17

I anchor into the Earth and unfold my energy outwards

WEDNESDAY 18

I am learning how to accept myself completely

THURSDAY 19

FRIDAY 20

I breathe in peace and breathe out stress and tension

SATURDAY 21

I bring my awareness into the present moment

SUNDAY 22

I give myself permission to be at peace with myself

MONDAY 23

TUESDAY 24

I am grateful for all of my relationships

WEDNESDAY 25

I slow down and connect to my heart

THURSDAY 26

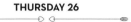

I am becoming my own best friend

FRIDAY 27

It is safe to experience all of my emotions

SATURDAY 28

I connect to a source of kindness and I am kind to myself

SUNDAY 29

I am able to say the things that I need to say

MONDAY 30

I am more peaceful when I am true to myself

TUESDAY 31

I walk away from drama and choose peace instead

NOTES ON GROUNDING AND HEALING

March

LOOK BACK ON THE MONTH AND REMEMBER A DIFFICULT SITUATION WHERE YOU WERE NOT GROUNDED, AND ONE WHERE YOU WERE GROUNDED – WHAT WAS DIFFERENT?

HOW WILL YOU REMEMBER TO GROUND YOURSELF NEXT TIME?

COMPASSION AND SELF-CARE

Self-care does not mean pampering. It could mean screaming at the wind or punching a pillow if that is what's called for. Compassion means a gentle awareness and a loving presence.
Neither of these things are ever selfish.

'how you love yourself is how you teach others to love you'

Rupi Kaur

APRIL

I often hear the words compassion and self-care. This month I will learn what they actually mean to me. By letting go of the guilt and fear associated with the idea that looking after myself is selfish, I can step into a caregiver role and start to give myself more of what it is I need. I will endeavour to make the time to sit and be with myself as I am, without needing to constantly be distracted. I know that I feel better, brighter and happier when I am nicer to me. I am learning that the biggest struggle I have with life is the struggle I have with myself. Once I let that go, life may still bring its surprises, but I will be stronger and move through them with grace. The quality of my life lies in my own hands; the quality of my thoughts and deeds impacts my every moment, and when I treat myself with care and compassion my whole life improves.

EXERCISE

I quiet my mind and bring my awareness into my body. I take the time to slow down and reassure myself that I can disconnect from everything outside of me for a few minutes. As I breathe, I feel the ground beneath me and the sky above me, and I can begin to let go of tension. After a few breaths I notice where my body is tight, and I breathe with that part of my body. I speak to it – tell it that I see it, that I know it is doing its best. I tell myself that everything is as it should be; that there is no need to fix or change anything; that all I need to do right now is release the pressure I put on myself, and I sink into a state of comfortable relaxation.

GOING DEEPER

While in your relaxed state, speak these four statements out loud: 'I'm sorry', 'Please forgive me', 'Thank you', 'I love you'. Notice how your body responds to each one. Let yourself sink into the energy of the words. Repeat them as a mantra and do this often.

WEDNESDAY 1

It is important to look after myself

THURSDAY 2

FRIDAY 3

Giving myself what I need is self-care

SATURDAY 4

I see myself and all that I have experienced, and I appreciate how far I have come

SUNDAY 5

I give myself permission to take some time for me today

MONDAY 6

TUESDAY 7

When I am kind to myself, I have more kindness to offer other people

WEDNESDAY 8

I am learning how to look after myself

THURSDAY 9

I will show up for myself and do what is needed

FRIDAY 10

Just for today, I will release all of the pressure I put on myself

SATURDAY 11

I accept myself completely, just as I am

SUNDAY 12

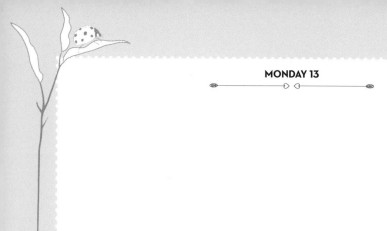

MONDAY 13

TUESDAY 14

I allow myself to make mistakes and learn from them

WEDNESDAY 15

I am learning how to give myself more of the things that I enjoy

THURSDAY 16

I feel safe to let go of old anger and pain

FRIDAY 17

I breathe in a source of compassion, I breathe out tightness and stress

SATURDAY 18

I no longer need to punish myself for anything I did or didn't do

SUNDAY 19

I don't need to compare myself to anyone else

MONDAY 20

I don't need to compare myself to anyone else

TUESDAY 21

I am enough just as I am

WEDNESDAY 22

I am grateful for this opportunity to get to know myself

THURSDAY 23

I allow myself to shine my light out into the world

FRIDAY 24

I open the door to let joy and happiness into my life

SATURDAY 25

I let go of my need to control the situation

SUNDAY 26

I give other people the freedom that I also give to myself

MONDAY 27

I feel safe to experience all of my emotions

TUESDAY 28

I give myself the benefit of the doubt

WEDNESDAY 29

I disconnect from everything outside of me and I come back to my centre

THURSDAY 30

I am learning how to love myself more

REVIEW YOUR INTENTION FOR THE YEAR

IS THERE ANYTHING YOU WISH TO CHANGE? REWRITE IT NOW, IN YOUR OWN WORDS.

April

THINK ABOUT A TIME WHEN YOU FELT BRIGHT AND HAPPY IN YOUR LIFE – HOW OLD WERE YOU? WHAT WAS THAT LIKE FOR YOU? WRITE ABOUT THAT PART OF YOU, WHAT YOU REMEMBER ABOUT YOURSELF, AND HOW YOU COULD BRING SOME MORE OF THAT ENERGY INTO YOUR LIFE RIGHT NOW.

NOW THINK ABOUT A TIME WHEN YOU FELT BURDENED BY LIFE, WHERE DOING NICE THINGS FOR YOURSELF WAS NOT ALLOWED. KNOWING WHAT YOU NOW KNOW, WHAT WOULD YOU SAY TO THAT PART OF YOU RIGHT NOW?

MAY

LOVE AND HAPPINESS

I had a dream someone left flowers at my doorstep. When I woke up I realised that it was me.

'Sometimes I need only to stand
wherever I am to be blessed.'

Mary Oliver

MAY

Now that I am no longer afraid to sit with myself, just as I am, I feel more at peace and open to let love in. I am learning that love has many dimensions. I do not need a 'special someone' to give love to me. Once I feel safe, I can let love in, and that in itself makes me happy and free. I open to happiness moment to moment, allowing myself to really enjoy it without going to look for it. I will continue to look after myself and each day I notice the benefit of the work I have done. I am feeling more in control of my emotions, more stable and present in the moment, and more aware of the choices I am making. This month I will focus on being in the present moment, feeling the Earth beneath my feet and allowing love into my life.

EXERCISE

I sit and relax and breathe and bring my awareness into the present moment. I breathe in a source of love and let it flow around my body, and I breathe out stress and tension. I now allow myself to notice the layers I have put around myself as protection from the world. I focus on the layers around my whole body, and with every breath I connect to one of them, soften it, melt it away, and let it go.

GOING DEEPER

Once you have released a few of these layers, notice how you are feeling. Now bring your awareness into your heart centre and be with how your heart is feeling. Is it hard or soft, closed or open? Gently breathe some loving intention into your heart. Don't force or push, just allow your heart to soften and open, just like a flower.

FRIDAY 1

Happiness starts with me

SATURDAY 2

.

SUNDAY 3

I fill my day with things that make me happy

MONDAY 4

Today I will notice the beauty all around me

TUESDAY 5

It is safe to give and to receive love

WEDNESDAY 6

THURSDAY 7

I begin and end my day with peace

FRIDAY 8

I breathe in love and I breathe out all that is not love

SATURDAY 9

I am learning how to love myself more

SUNDAY 10

I deliberately fill everything I do with love

MONDAY 11

I am compassionate and kind to myself

TUESDAY 12

WEDNESDAY 13

I feel the ground beneath my feet and I pull my awareness back into my body

THURSDAY 14

I look forward to what this day may bring

FRIDAY 15

Today I will make time for fun

SATURDAY 16

SUNDAY 17

I make the space to do the things I need to do

MONDAY 18

I am grateful for all the love in my life

TUESDAY 19

I shine my light outwards and spread love and happiness to the world

WEDNESDAY 20

I can make difficult choices with a loving heart

THURSDAY 21

I leave a trail of love behind me

FRIDAY 22

I bring my awareness back to my heart and fill my heart with love

SATURDAY 23

SUNDAY 24

When I am centred and in the present moment, I can choose how to respond

MONDAY 25

I let go of my resistance to love

TUESDAY 26

Today I choose to enjoy the good things

WEDNESDAY 27

Love softens all of my sharp edges

THURSDAY 28

I no longer need to criticise myself

FRIDAY 29

I give permission to release all of the blocks in my heart and let love in

SATURDAY 30

SUNDAY 31

When I slow down I can feel the love that is here for me

NOTES ON LOVE AND HAPPINESS

May

WAS YOUR DAY DIFFERENT WHEN YOU SENT AN INTENTION FOR JOY? HOW?
WHAT WERE THE DIFFICULTIES YOU ENCOUNTERED WHEN YOU WERE FEELING HAPPY?

WHAT ARE YOUR REMAINING BLOCKS TO LOVE?
HOW CAN YOU WORK TOWARDS RELEASING THEM?

JUNE

AWAKENING

Awakening occurs when you release the
lies you were telling yourself and shed the layers of doubt
and fear and know, really know, that love exists and
that you are worthy of it.

'Truth destroys the world you
used to live in.'

Neil Kramer

JUNE

The work I have already done this year has given me a strong foundation from which to build upon. As I get more certain of who I am becoming I realise that some of the things in my life no longer resonate with me; some of them actually make me feel heavy, weak or ill. With brave, fresh eyes I can look at my reality and see what is here in front of me when perhaps before I was unable to. Releasing the pressure that I put on myself while acknowledging and working with my inner wisdom will be my key focus for this month. I will find myself returning time and time again to my centre as what needs to be healed or let go of is revealed to me. I see this month as an opportunity for good and healthy change; to take the risk and to shrug off the things that no longer fit for me. I am safe, I am here, I can do this.

EXERCISE

I slow down and use my imagination to see myself unhooking from everything that is outside of me. I bring myself into my body and into the present moment. I am whole and I am here, right now, in this moment. I am safe, I am at peace. I breathe in peace, I breathe out everything that is not peace. I breathe in peace, I breathe out everything that is not peace.

GOING DEEPER

List five things that you know are true. Then ask yourself are they really true, or are they just true for you. Realise that your ideas of what is true may not match what is really true, and that there is a greater truth than what you believe to be true. Allow your mind to open and let go of your fixed ideas, so that you stretch and grow.

MONDAY 1

It is safe for me to feel all of my emotions

TUESDAY 2

WEDNESDAY 3

My emotions are not me, they are just passing through me

THURSDAY 4

I connect to my inner wisdom and know that the answer lies within

FRIDAY 5

I am ready to live my most authentic life

SATURDAY 6

Just for today I will focus on gratitude

SUNDAY 7

No matter what is going on around me, I can always bring myself back to my centre

MONDAY 8

I accept myself just as I am, and I can accept others just as they are

TUESDAY 9

WEDNESDAY 10

Today I will make time to connect to a source of peace

THURSDAY 11

I deliberately choose what feels good and true to me

FRIDAY 12

I take the time to listen to my intuition and act upon it where necessary

I am learning how to do what I say, and say what I do

SUNDAY 14

I will never abandon myself

MONDAY 15

I do not need to get involved in other people's drama

TUESDAY 16

WEDNESDAY 17

I trust the Universe is supporting me in mysterious ways

THURSDAY 18

I can tell the difference between what I need and what I want

FRIDAY 19

Today I will love and protect my inner child

SATURDAY 20

I allow myself to express my truth in many different ways

SUNDAY 21

It is okay to ask for help

MONDAY 22

I allow myself to grow and change in all dimensions

TUESDAY 23

WEDNESDAY 24

I feel my feet on the ground and I am here

THURSDAY 25

I deliberately make time for beautiful things

FRIDAY 26

SATURDAY 27

I connect to a source of nature and feel held

SUNDAY 28

I breathe in love and breathe out all that is not love

MONDAY 29

I am not afraid to feel difficult emotions

TUESDAY 30

I feel better when I am true to myself

NOTES ON AWAKENING

June

CONGRUENCE MEANS THINKING AND FEELING THE SAME THING, INSIDE AND OUT. WHERE IN YOUR LIFE ARE YOU BEING CONGRUENT? WHERE ARE YOU NOT BEING CONGRUENT? WHAT CAN YOU DO TO CHANGE THIS?

AUTHENTICITY IS WHEN YOU SPEAK THE WORDS YOU REALLY FEEL, INSTEAD OF HIDING AWAY FROM THEM. NOW THAT YOU ARE FAMILIAR WITH HOW YOU REALLY FEEL, WHAT CAN YOU DO TO SUPPORT YOURSELF BECOMING EVEN MORE AUTHENTIC WITH EVERY WORD AND DEED?

EXPANSION AND GROWTH

Trying to fit in can be painful, but when you enlarge, you can hold the whole world in your heart.

'Why are you so determined to keep your wild silently inside you? Let it breathe. Give it a voice. Let it roll out of you on the wide open waves. Set it free.'

Jeanette LeBlanc

JULY

I have grown and changed. It is halfway through the year and I can really see how far I've come. I trust myself more and I feel more centred and calm. I listen to my intuition and I am not afraid to take action from there. This month I give myself more space to breathe, to grow and to think. Healing is not an easy process. I recognise my inner struggle and I will give that more space too. I am ready to step into my authentic life. I know this is the best way forward for me, and for the ones that I love. I'm noticing my authenticity is being reciprocated in my relationships. It is becoming easier to say how I feel and to make the space to listen in return. I am able to agree to disagree with some people, and to still be at peace with myself. The quality of my life is changing for the better. I'm excited for what this month will bring.

EXERCISE

I take an imaginary pencil and draw a boundary line around myself. I see it as a wall, a few bricks high, and I take some time with the image until it feels like it's the perfect size and distance away from me. As I breathe out, I soften my body; as I breathe in, I bring my awareness into my centre. In my mind I push the boundary wall a little bit further out from my body and come into balance with taking up more space in the world.

GOING DEEPER

Once you are comfortable with the size of your boundary wall, allow yourself to notice if there are any people you have a relationship with inside the walls with you. One at a time, say thank you to each person for caring so deeply for you, and then gently push them to the opposite side of the wall. If you like, you can imagine a gate or a doorway in your wall. Tell that person that if they want access to you, they have to knock at the door and get your permission before they enter.

WEDNESDAY 1

I bring my awareness into my heart and I can say what I need to say with love

THURSDAY 2

FRIDAY 3

I slow down and bring my awareness into the moment

SATURDAY 4

I forgive myself for my mistakes and I let them go

SUNDAY 5

Like a butterfly, I see myself hatch out of my cocoon and spread my wings

MONDAY 6

TUESDAY 7

I can observe what no longer fits for me without judgement

WEDNESDAY 8

I do not need to fix or change anything today

THURSDAY 9

When I am patient with myself, I am more patient with others

FRIDAY 10

I hand my troubles over to the Universe for safekeeping

SATURDAY 11

SUNDAY 12

I slow down and make space for what it is I am feeling today

MONDAY 13

I take the time I need each day to reconnect to my heart

TUESDAY 14

I have good, strong, energetic boundaries

WEDNESDAY 15

I separate my mind from my heart and listen to each in turn

THURSDAY 16

FRIDAY 17

I allow myself to express myself in many different and creative ways

SATURDAY 18

As I grow and expand, I attract more love and joy into my life

SUNDAY 19

I catch myself when I take things personally and then let it go

MONDAY 20

I step away from drama, breathe and reconnect to love

TUESDAY 21

With love in my heart I can say no to things that are not good for me

WEDNESDAY 22

I accept myself just as I am and I accept others just as they are

THURSDAY 23

Today I will make time to be joyful

FRIDAY 24

I feel the freedom of being completely at peace with myself

SATURDAY 25

I am loving and kind to myself and others

SUNDAY 26

MONDAY 27

Every experience is an opportunity for learning

TUESDAY 28

I make time to do the things that I love

WEDNESDAY 29

I no longer need to cause myself emotional pain

THURSDAY 30

FRIDAY 31

I am worthy and I am enough, just as I am

NOTES ON EXPANSION AND GROWTH

July

WHAT IS THE MOST DIFFICULT THING ABOUT GROWTH? HOW CAN YOU SUPPORT YOURSELF
DURING A GROWTH PHASE?

HOW DID YOU MANAGE WITH THE BOUNDARY EXERCISE? WHO KEEPS BREAKING INTO YOUR
BOUNDARIES? WHAT DO YOU NEED TO DO SO YOU CAN BE STRONGER?

EXPANSION AND GROWTH

BALANCE AND STABILITY

We are always in flow, we are always in motion. The key is to find equilibrium, the still point, so you always feel the ground beneath your feet.

'Getting in balance is not so much about adopting new strategies to change your behaviours, as it is about realigning yourself in all of your thoughts so as to create a balance between what you desire and how you conduct your life on a daily basis.'

Wayne Dyer

AUGUST

I can see how my world is shifting to match my new way of being. Instead of moving too quickly this month, I will invest some time to focus on stability and balance. I am learning that balance is a constant process of ups and downs over time. I see that I can better hold myself during difficult times and that I am really allowing myself to enjoy the good things too. I will look at my life and fine-tune my choices, my attitudes and beliefs so that they are stronger and more solid inside me. I will also make time to focus on gratitude and appreciation for all the work I have done and am still doing. When I let go of my attachments to how I think things should be, I can better ride the waves, the ups and the downs, sometimes surfing, sometimes swimming, but now I know that I will not drown.

EXERCISE

I imagine that I am in the sea and allow the sea to show me the current state of my emotions. I let go of my need to stand and feel my feet on the bottom, and I allow myself to feel buoyant and free as the waves carry me wherever they will. When it is wild and tumultuous, I surf the waves, bobbing over the tops, sometimes getting splashed, but I know that I will be okay. When it is serene, I float, calm and gentle. I can see through the water and the magic of the life that's inside. I feel free and at peace knowing that I have mastered a part of myself that will always be with me no matter what.

GOING DEEPER

Imagine diving deep beneath the waves to a source of stillness and calm. There is always stillness here. Let your mind still, your body still. Let go of your troubles; the sea can hold them for you. It is safe for you to just be, right here, right now, for as long as you want to be.

SATURDAY 1

I am allowed to feel difficult emotions

SUNDAY 2

I have everything I need already inside me

MONDAY 3

I bring my mind, heart and inner wisdom into alignment

TUESDAY 4

WEDNESDAY 5

I use my breath to slow down my thoughts

THURSDAY 6

I check my energetic boundaries and enlarge and clear my energetic space

FRIDAY 7

I connect to a source of compassion and kindness for myself and others

SATURDAY 8

I am grateful for this opportunity to be alive

SUNDAY 9

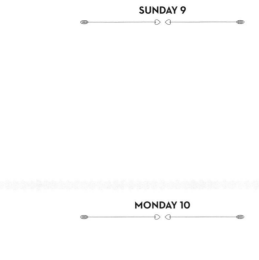

MONDAY 10

I let go of the things that I cannot change and bring myself back to myself

TUESDAY 11

Today I will make the time to rest and laugh and play

WEDNESDAY 12

I no longer need to struggle with myself

THURSDAY 13

I am grateful for my body and how much work it does for me in the background

FRIDAY 14

I am ready to invite in my happiest life now

SATURDAY 15

I am not afraid to be excited and learn new things

SUNDAY 16

MONDAY 17

I open to receive the love that is here for me

TUESDAY 18

I am grateful for all of my relationships and the lessons and joy that they bring

WEDNESDAY 19

THURSDAY 20

I am learning how to accept all the parts of myself

FRIDAY 21

I move through the day with compassion and love

SATURDAY 22

I can ride the waves of emotion and experience all of it

SUNDAY 23

I ask for the skills and the tools that I need to look after myself

MONDAY 24

TUESDAY 25

I am grateful for all of the opportunities that come my way

WEDNESDAY 26

THURSDAY 27

I see the beauty in small and ordinary things

FRIDAY 28

I allow myself to enjoy the pleasures of my senses

SATURDAY 29

I enjoy life much more when I am at peace with myself

SUNDAY 30

I no longer need to get tangled up to please someone else

MONDAY 31

I look after my mind, my body, my emotions and my soul

NOTES ON BALANCE AND STABILITY

August

IMAGINE THAT YOU'RE GOING BACK IN TIME TO VISIT YOURSELF AT AGE SEVEN. WHAT WERE YOUR HOPES AND DREAMS BACK THEN? WHAT DID YOU WANT TO BE WHEN YOU GREW UP? WRITE DOWN SOME ADVICE FOR YOUR YOUNGER SELF THAT WOULD REALLY HELP YOU ON THE WAY.

WHAT IS IT LIKE FOR YOU TO READ BACK ON THIS ADVICE? DO YOU SEE HOW FAR YOU HAVE COME NOW? PREPARING FOR THE NEXT MONTH OF FUN AND LAUGHTER, BRING YOUR SEVEN-YEAR-OLD SELF WITH YOU FOR THE RIDE.

FUN AND LAUGHTER

When you celebrate life, you shine at your brightest. Making time for fun and laughter is more important for your health than you may think.

'Laughter is a gift from God that opens our hearts. Laughing heals our hearts and brings us together.'

Eileen Anglin

SEPTEMBER

It is time for me to allow fun, joy and laughter wholeheartedly into my life. For many years I have been surviving, guarding my emotions, in fear of expressing myself in case I hurt someone or was rejected. I look around me and I notice many people living the same way. The world needs more joy; we cannot expect fun and laughter to come to us if we do not create it ourselves or welcome it in. I give my full permission for lightness and joy to enter my life at a deeper level. This month I want to feel the richness and expansion of my life and my inner light that comes through enjoying my life. I let go of guilt and fear and I become a beacon that shines outwards, spreading fun and laughter into the world. I celebrate how far I have come, how much I have done, and how good it feels right now to be me.

EXERCISE

I imagine I am sitting on a park bench. I ask to meet the part of me that is afraid to really have fun and enjoy life. I feel them arrive and sit down beside me. I ask them to speak and I listen with compassion. When they have finished, I speak to them in turn. I say if I don't have fun, I am not honouring all of the work I have done. I tell them we are working hard for this and we deserve it. Our conversation ends with a hug or a handshake; they walk away and leave me on the bench. I gently bring my awareness back into the room where I am.

GOING DEEPER

Look at your appointment schedule for the month of September and book something fun to do each week, either with friends or on your own. It could be a pottery, dance or singing class, or a show or a night out at the movies. Leave your troubles outside and bring your full awareness into each activity and really allow yourself to enjoy it.

TUESDAY 1

I invite fun and laughter into my life

WEDNESDAY 2

Today I will move gracefully and lightly in the world

THURSDAY 3

Not everything needs to be taken seriously

FRIDAY 4

SATURDAY 5

I let go of the pressure I put upon myself and others

SUNDAY 6

I connect to a source of peace and breathe peace into my heart

MONDAY 7

I feel the ground beneath my feet, the sky above me and I am held

TUESDAY 8

I can step away from heaviness and find myself again

WEDNESDAY 9

THURSDAY 10

I check my energetic boundaries and expand and clear them as needed

FRIDAY 11

I am open to finding joy in unexpected places

SATURDAY 12

I allow myself to be happy in my life

FUN AND LAUGHTER

SUNDAY 13

I make time for work and I make time to play

MONDAY 14

Today I am inviting my inner child to spend the day with me

TUESDAY 15

I am learning how to really enjoy the good things in life

WEDNESDAY 16

THURSDAY 17

I am safe, I am centred, I am grounded, I am here

FRIDAY 18

I let go of my need to get it exactly right every time

SATURDAY 19

I disconnect from my ideas of who I 'should' be

SUNDAY 20

I am experiencing the flow of life

MONDAY 21

I no longer need to feel guilty about feeling happy

TUESDAY 22

I can hear the strength and quality of my presence when I laugh

WEDNESDAY 23

I open my heart to look for the magic in the world

THURSDAY 24

Life is a miracle. I am grateful for the chance to experience it all

FRIDAY 25

I listen to my heart and I give it what it needs

SATURDAY 26

SUNDAY 27

I let go of my worries and bring myself into the present moment

MONDAY 28

I allow myself to feel what I am feeling and then I let it go

TUESDAY 29

Today I say 'Yes!' to life

WEDNESDAY 30

REVIEW YOUR INTENTION FOR THE YEAR

WRITE A NEW INTENTION FOR THE REST OF THIS YEAR

September

DO YOU FIND IT EASIER BEING WITH EMOTIONAL PAIN THAN BEING WITH FUN AND LAUGHTER? WHERE DO YOU THINK THAT COMES FROM?

WHAT CAN YOU DO TO CLEAR WHAT IS IN THE WAY OF ALLOWING YOURSELF TO HAVE A MORE JOYFUL LIFE?

AUTHENTICITY AND TRUTH

Being truthful inside and out is not an easy path, yet we have all been carrying the burden of lies for too long.

'It takes courage to grow up and become who you really are.'

E.E. Cummings

OCTOBER

When something is not true for me, I feel it in my body as tightness in my chest, or heaviness in my stomach. As I grow and heal, I realise this feeling also holds for what I tell myself, as well as when I compromise myself to 'keep the peace'. After all the work I've done I know I don't need to pretend anything to myself anymore. This month I will notice when I hide a truth from myself, realise that it's just an old habit, and let it go. I will also notice when I speak untruths to keep other people happy. I realise that it may just be what I think they want to hear, rather than what they actually want to hear. I also know it's the 'old me' in action. I want to be true to my heart and live a wholehearted life. Sometimes I may need to rectify what I say or do. Other times it may be easier to stay quiet, but over the coming days and weeks I will be stronger in my truth than before, lighter in my body and a conduit for happiness and joy.

EXERCISE

I catch myself when I say things that are not true for me – saying sorry when I'm not sorry, or agreeing to something when I don't really agree. I notice how my body feels when I say these words, particularly when I call myself a name out of frustration or anger. I know that words have power; now I see how they affect me directly. I will take my list of words and create an antidote for each. I commit to replacing angry words for peaceful ones, negative ones for positive ones. I want to feel lighter in my body when I speak. I will no longer hurt myself with words.

GOING DEEPER

Think of a time where you felt pushed into a corner and had to say something you didn't feel was true for you. Replay the memory in your mind. What would you have preferred to say? Write down the truthful statement – when else can you use this? What other situations would it be useful to do this for?

THURSDAY 1

I let go of my expectations and see things as they really are

FRIDAY 2

I am not my thoughts, I am not my emotions; I am the shining light beneath

SATURDAY 3

I no longer need to cause myself emotional pain

SUNDAY 4

MONDAY 5

I forgive myself for everything I have done or not done in my life

TUESDAY 6

I bring more of my presence into the world

WEDNESDAY 7

I release all of the pressure that I put upon myself to always be right

THURSDAY 8

I allow myself to let love into my heart

FRIDAY 9

SATURDAY 10

I make the time to quiet my mind and listen to my inner wisdom

SUNDAY 11

I feel the Earth beneath me and the sky above me and I feel held

MONDAY 12

When I connect to the Earth I feel more centred and calm

TUESDAY 13

I am free to be completely who I am in this moment

WEDNESDAY 14

When I slow down, I can express how I feel in this moment without fear

THURSDAY 15

I look for the learning and the gifts in every situation

FRIDAY 16

SATURDAY 17

I listen to my body and give it what it needs

SUNDAY 18

What is true for me may not be true for you, and that's okay

MONDAY 19

I am grateful for all of my relationships

TUESDAY 20

I slow down and breathe and connect to an inner source of peace

WEDNESDAY 21

I pull all of my energy out from things outside of me and bring it back into me

THURSDAY 22

I spend time creating good, strong, energetic boundaries

FRIDAY 23

SATURDAY 24

I deliberately surround myself with things that lift me

SUNDAY 25

I give myself the space I need to process my difficult emotions

MONDAY 26

TUESDAY 27

When I let go of things I no longer need, I make more space for joy

WEDNESDAY 28

I invite more joy into my life

THURSDAY 29

I allow myself to show up for life

FRIDAY 30

When my light shines brightly it reminds others they can shine theirs brightly too

SATURDAY 31

NOTES ON AUTHENTICITY AND TRUTH

October

DESCRIBE YOUR JOURNEY WITH THE MOST DIFFICULT THING YOU LEARNED THIS MONTH.

WHAT ARE YOU STILL WORKING ON? WHO CAN YOU ASK FOR HELP WITH THIS?

TRUST AND FAITH

When we let go of our need to control the situation, we move into flow with the Universe and open the door for wonderful things to come into our lives.

'Observation of the world around us reveals many instances of order and self-organised systems of great complexity, one nested in another. There must be forces and processes at work to bring them into being.'

Richard Golden

NOVEMBER

In my quiet moments I feel the presence of something greater than myself. When I feel safe and relaxed, I allow my heart to open and I feel a deep sense of peace. I have been hurt by life's experiences but I am healing more and more each day. I am learning to improve the quality of all the choices I am making, also in word and deed. Being on this path has brought me great strength and solace and now I am ready to let more love into my life. When I ask the Universe for a sign that I am on the right path I see them everywhere. Some days I have such synchronicities I know that they cannot be accidental. I have trust and faith that there is a source of pure, unconditional love that everyone can have access to. This month I set my intention to really experience unconditional love, to feel my connection to the Universe expand and to shine my light out into the world.

EXERCISE

I imagine that I am a radio, tuning into the frequency of love. I take my time to do it wholeheartedly and I know when I have connected because I feel a flow of energy in my body. I ground myself if I get lightheaded, and then I breathe love in through my lungs. I can feel it flowing through my body and I breathe out all that is not love into the ground through my feet. I breathe and I can feel the love flowing into my heart, up and over my shoulders, down my arms and out of my hands. Everything I touch I fill with love.

GOING DEEPER

Take the exercise from above and go further – breathe in love and see your heart shining brightly outwards from you like the sun. Expand the sun so that it sends beams of love towards someone you care about. Imagine they receive it, smile and are lifted. Let go of that image and breathe. Now send it to someone you're having difficulty with. Let go of that image, then send it to someone you've never met. Let go of the image and enjoy the feeling of the energy flowing in your body.

SUNDAY 1

I am here, right now, in this moment

MONDAY 2

TUESDAY 3

I feel grounded and safe

WEDNESDAY 4

I trust that all is exactly as it should be

I let go of my need to fix or change anyone

FRIDAY 6

I do not need to know all of the answers

SATURDAY 7

Today I will follow my truth by following my heart

SUNDAY 8

I let go of control and allow things to fall into place as they will

MONDAY 9

I trust that I am looked after by the Universe

TUESDAY 10

When I let go of my expectations I step into the flow of life

WEDNESDAY 11

THURSDAY 12

I will never have all of the answers and that is okay

FRIDAY 13

I slow down and breathe and let love into my heart

SATURDAY 14

I give myself whatever I need to bring myself into balance

SUNDAY 15

I choose to look at life through the eyes of love

MONDAY 16

TUESDAY 17

I let go of my need to always be right

WEDNESDAY 18

There is enough love here for everyone

THURSDAY 19

I trust that everything will work out as it should

FRIDAY 20

I take the time I need to look after myself

SATURDAY 21

When I am at peace, I stop struggling with life

SUNDAY 22

I breathe in love and breathe out all that is not love

MONDAY 23

I hand my troubles over to the Universe and I feel the burden lifting off me

TUESDAY 24

I listen to my inner wisdom and take action where needed

WEDNESDAY 25

I choose to look for the peace and beauty in everything

THURSDAY 26

FRIDAY 27

I release myself and others from my expectations

SATURDAY 28

I slow down and reconnect to my heart

SUNDAY 29

I feel safe to relax and enjoy my life

MONDAY 30

WHAT I WOULD LIKE THE UNIVERSE TO TAKE CARE OF FOR ME:

DID YOU ASK FOR A SIGN THAT YOU'RE ON THE RIGHT PATH THIS MONTH? OR THIS YEAR? WHAT WAS
THE SIGN AND WHERE DID YOU SEE IT? HOW DID YOU FEEL WHEN YOU SAW IT? IF YOU DIDN'T SEE IT,
TAKE A FEW MOMENTS AND COME INTO YOUR BODY AND ASK YOUR INNER WISDOM WHAT YOU NEED
TO DO SO THAT YOU'RE MORE AVAILABLE AND IN THE FLOW OF LIFE.

DECEMBER

INSPIRATION AND CREATIVITY

It has not been an easy journey, but it has been a courageous one. Here you stand, more whole than you have ever been, true to yourself – heart expanded and wings outstretched. You have the pure potential to do anything you want and live a wholehearted life. Well done!

'Each of us is an artist of our days; the greater our integrity and awareness, the more original and creative our time will become.'

John O'Donohue

DECEMBER

This is the last month of the year. I'm so grateful for all the learning I have embodied.
I move, act and think differently. I bring more grace and presence into everything I
do. I am more authentic and free. I will no longer silence my voice and I do not need
validation from others to express myself. My boundaries are better; I have more
energy and my relationships have improved. This month I am excited to invite the
creative aspect of me to awaken. I allow myself to become inspired by beauty, nature,
art, music, poetry and my relationships. I do not need to be an accomplished artist
to express my joy, hope and gratitude for my life. The more at peace I am, the more
life flows through me, and I imagine what I can create when I feel free and light and
in vibrant health. I am no longer surviving. I am living – there are colours in my day,
there is magic in my world. This month I will celebrate all of the work I have done, and
all of that which is yet to come.

EXERCISE

I slow down and breathe and connect to my heart. I breathe from my stomach
and I feel the ground beneath my feet. I think about how far I have come and I am
grateful. I breathe in gratitude and I let go of heaviness and emotional pain. I know
there is more to do. I allow my mind to become a cinema screen and I see pictures
and words appear. I can hear music; my soul sings. I have something to say: I am
important, I am loved. When I open my eyes I put pen to paper and write, or draw,
or play my music and dance. I am here, and my energy shines at its brightest when I
express myself freely and with love.

GOING DEEPER

Try something new this month, something you've never done before. Go to an
exhibition, take a class, or plan and carry out a ceremony. Bring your full presence
into the experience and enjoy it wholeheartedly.

TUESDAY 1

I am grateful that I am my own best friend

WEDNESDAY 2

THURSDAY 3

I give myself permission to express myself in many different ways

FRIDAY 4

I release my need for others to make me happy

SATURDAY 5

I thank the Universe for supporting me on my healing journey

SUNDAY 6

I release the pressure I put on myself to get things perfect

MONDAY 7

I feel safe to experiment and make mistakes

TUESDAY 8

I can spend time doing things I love without guilt

WEDNESDAY 9

THURSDAY 10

I am grateful for the feeling of freedom that comes with accepting myself completely

FRIDAY 11

When I appreciate other people's gifts and talents it gives me awareness of my own

SATURDAY 12

I open my heart to love and joy and I let life inspire me

SUNDAY 13

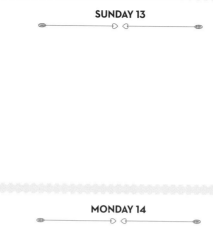

MONDAY 14

I give myself permission to follow the wisdom of my heart

TUESDAY 15

I am free to be myself completely

WEDNESDAY 16

I shine my light and fill the world with love and freedom

THURSDAY 17

I relish the smells, sounds, colours and tastes that I experience

FRIDAY 18

I am grateful for the opportunities that I experienced this year

SATURDAY 19

I am learning how to give myself more of the things that I love

SUNDAY 20

MONDAY 21

I am filled with joy and appreciation of the potential for my life

TUESDAY 22

I am learning how to be my best, healed self

WEDNESDAY 23

When I am true to myself, my body feels light and my energy is clear

THURSDAY 24

When I deliberately connect to a source of love, I feel happy and content

FRIDAY 25

I respect all human beings no matter where they are on their journey

SATURDAY 26

SUNDAY 27

I see the beauty in everything and I am grateful for my life

MONDAY 28

I create the space for new and beautiful things to come into my life

TUESDAY 29

When I let love and happiness into my heart I see them reflected back to me in my life

WEDNESDAY 30

THURSDAY 31

I am beginning to believe that anything is possible

NOTES ON INSPIRATION AND CREATIVITY

December

LOOK BACK OVER WHAT YOU HAVE WRITTEN IN THE DIARY OVER THE PAST YEAR. ARE YOU THE SAME
PERSON AS YOU WERE WHEN YOU BEGAN?

NOTICE HOW YOUR VOICE HAS CHANGED, HOW MUCH STRONGER AND SELF-CONFIDENT YOU ARE
NOW. HOW CAN YOU TELL? WHAT ARE THE BIGGEST THINGS THAT YOU'VE NOTICED?

2020

WHERE DO YOU FEEL YOUR WORK IS STILL UNFINISHED, AND WHY?

_____

_____

_____

_____

_____

_____

WHAT WERE THE BEST THINGS THAT YOU DID THIS PAST YEAR TO
SUPPORT YOURSELF DURING DIFFICULT TIMES?

_____

_____

_____

_____

_____

2020

WHAT WERE THE HIGHLIGHTS OF THE YEAR FOR YOU?

WHAT IS YOUR INTENTION FOR THE YEAR TO COME?

ACKNOWLEDGEMENTS

Huge thanks to Lorna Bevan for her consultation work which helped
establish the themes in this year's diary. You can find her at
www.hareinthemoonastrology.co.uk where she offers both general
and personal astrological readings. Gratitude goes to Sarah Liddy,
Commissioning Editor and co-creator at Gill Books, and to
Jane Matthews, designer supreme, for the beautiful design that
melds my words with the images so perfectly. I want to thank everyone
at Gill Books, particularly Ellen, Sheila, Paul, Deborah and Linda.
It's great to have you all behind this project. Finally, I want to thank my
family – Ian, Megan, Joshua, Mya, Siân and Milo. Thanks for being
there and always supporting me. When there is love in your heart, there
is love in your life.

ALSO BY THE AUTHOR

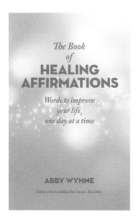

The Book
of
**HEALING
AFFIRMATIONS**

*Words to improve
your life,
one day at a time*

ABBY WYNNE

Author of the bestselling One Day at a Time Diary